Quick and Easy Math

FOR GRADES K-2

Tina Thoburn, Ed.D., and Terry Kane

Troll Associates

Interior illustrations by Gwen Connolly

ISBN: 0-8167-3272-8
Printed in the United States of America.
10 9 8 7 6 5 4 3 2 1

Metric Conversion Chart

1 inch = 2.54 cm
1 foot = .305 m
1 yard = .914 m
1 mile = 1.61 km
1 square mile = 2.6 square km
1 fluid ounce = 29.573 ml
1 dry ounce = 28.35 g
1 ton = .91 metric ton
1 gallon = 3.79 l
1 pound = 0.45 kg
1 cup = .24 l
1 pint = .473 l
1 teaspoon = 4.93 ml
1 tablespoon = 14.78 ml

Conversion from Fahrenheit to Celsius: subtract 32 and then multiply the remainder by 5/9.

☐ CONTENTS ☐

☐ INTRODUCTION ☐

Have you been looking for new games and activities to add spice to your math teaching? *Quick and Easy Math for Grades K-2* offers a smorgasbord of ideas that will enrich and reinforce math concepts for young children. Here you will find a variety of games, puzzles, and manipulative activities to help your students gain an understanding of numbers, geometry, and measurement as well as develop their abilities in problem solving and logical thinking. Imaginative reproducibles will provide your class with unique, challenging learning aids that are fun to complete.

One of the main objectives of early math instruction is to help children develop number sense—that is, an understanding of what numbers are, how they are represented, how they can be compared, and how they are affected by different operations. To this end, many of the activities in *Quick and Easy Math for Grades K-2* focus on reading and writing whole numbers, comparing them, and adding and subtracting them. From the jungle, to the farm, to outer space, children encounter weird and wonderful creatures to help them along on their number-learning adventures. Even fractional numbers are investigated in several activities designed around one of children's favorite subjects, food. How can they resist using fractions to order pizza or to detect what part of a cake is missing?

Young children love to play with geometric shapes. With *Quick and Easy Math for Grades K-2*, they will enjoy exploring shapes, symmetry, and mirror images. And you will appreciate the curriculum tie-in with social studies, as your students learn to follow map directions.

Measurement activities provide children with hands-on experiences. Money and time are presented through both real-life and imaginary buying and selling experiences. Special groups of lessons are provided on classification, patterns, and statistics.

Many activities provide special opportunities for children to work together as they manipulate concrete materials and talk about what they are doing and discovering. A number of activities are open-ended to encourage creative thinking and extension of math ideas. Children of varying needs and abilities will find much here to feed their hunger for new learning or to confirm their mastery of familiar concepts.

It Takes All Sorts

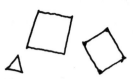

Objective: Classifying shapes

What You Need:

a copy of the **reproducible** on page 9 for each child

2 pencils of different lengths

scissors

blue and red crayons for each child

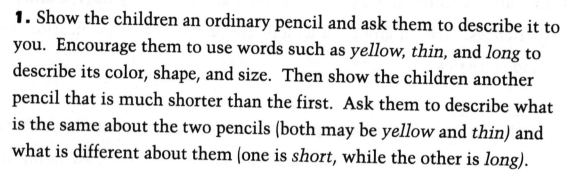

What You Do:

1. Show the children an ordinary pencil and ask them to describe it to you. Encourage them to use words such as *yellow*, *thin*, and *long* to describe its color, shape, and size. Then show the children another pencil that is much shorter than the first. Ask them to describe what is the same about the two pencils (both may be *yellow* and *thin)* and what is different about them (one is *short*, while the other is *long)*.

2. Now distribute copies of the **reproducible** on page 9 to the children. Ask them to color the shapes in the top two rows red and the shapes in the bottom two rows blue. Help the children cut apart the squares so that each child has a set of attribute tiles.

3. Point out that the tiles can be sorted by size, by shape, or by color. First, have children sort the tiles by color, making a blue pile and a red pile. Then have them mix all the tiles together again and sort them next by size so that they have a pile of large shapes and a pile of small shapes. Finally, have them sort the tiles by shape, making a pile of circles, a pile of squares, and a pile of triangles.

Attribute Tiles

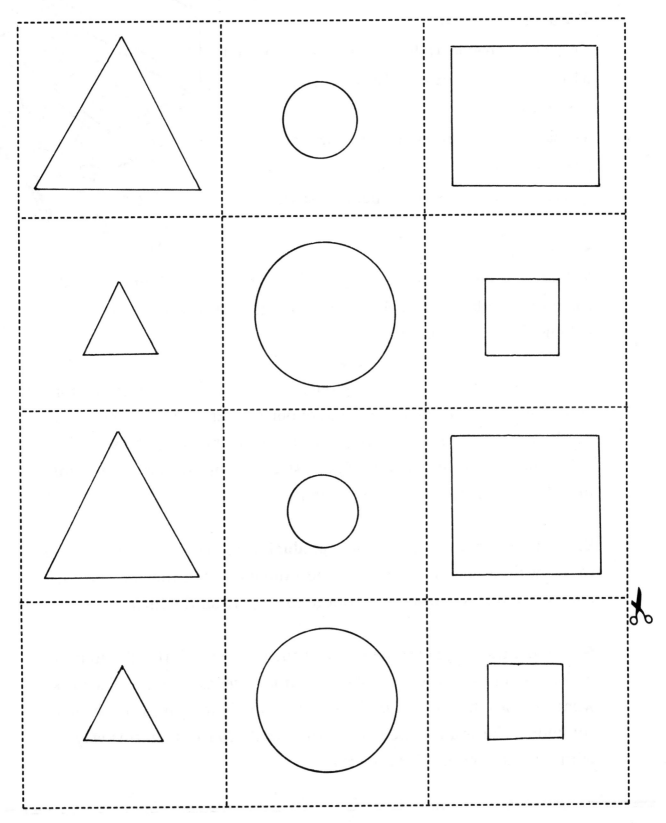

Get Ready, Get Set

Objective: Grouping objects into sets

What You Need:

a copy of the **reproducible** on page 11 for each child

a baseball, a ball of yarn, and a ball of clay

4–6 egg cartons

4–6 bags, each containing an assortment of small objects

a large selection of crayons for children to share

several pairs of scissors for children to share

What You Do:

1. Show the children a baseball, a ball of yarn, and a ball of clay. Ask them to describe each object and to name the set to which they all belong (the set of *round* things).

2. Now organize the class into groups. Give each group an egg carton and a bag containing an assortment of objects. Encourage students to think of as many ways of sorting the objects as they can—by size, color, shape, texture, use, etc. Then ask the groups to sort their items into the egg carton sections by attribute.

3. Next, distribute copies of the **reproducible** on page 11. Ask children to select three colors and to color the animal on each tile one of those colors. Help them cut their attribute tiles apart on the lines.

4. Use the tiles to play some sorting games. First, ask the children to make a set of those tiles that show "animals wearing a tie." Then ask what the tiles that are *not* in the set of "animals wearing a tie" have in common. (The animals are *not* wearing ties.) Continue in this way with other attributes of the animals.

This Piggy Wore a Tie

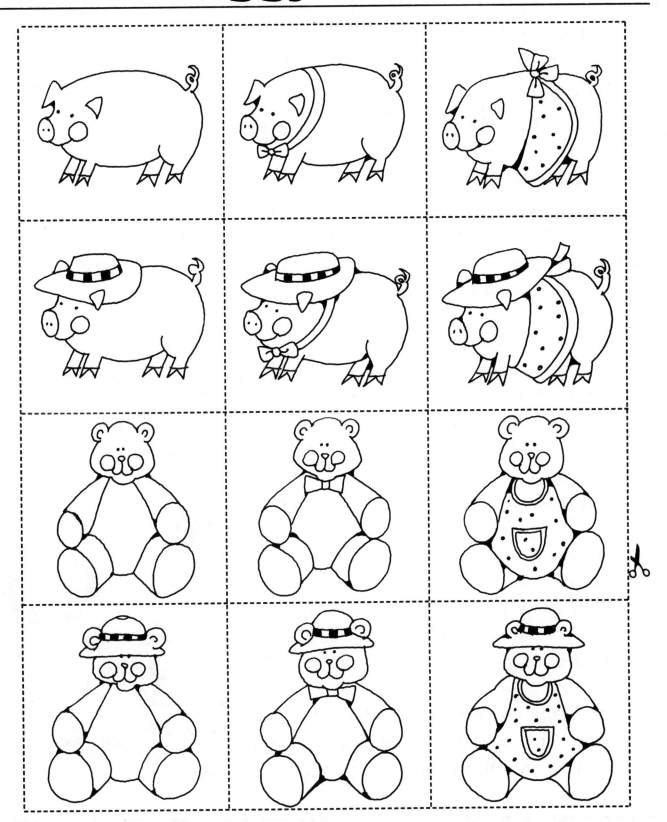

One, Two, Buckle My Shoe

Objective: Understanding number order from 0 to 10

What You Need:

a copy of the **reproducible** on page 13 for each child

4-6 bags, each containing 10 all-of-a-kind objects
   (One bag might contain 10 miniature toys;
   another could hold 10 erasers or buttons, for example.)

What You Do:

1. Ask children to name some ways that people use numbers every day. Then ask them to think of some things people might not be able to do without numbers. (We would not be able to measure things or count money to buy things, for example.)

2. Now set up the bags of objects in front of the class and invite a pair of children to come up. First, ask one child to pull out several objects from one of the bags and show them to the other child. The second child must then select the same number of objects from the second bag. Ask: "How can we tell if the number of objects in each group is the same?" Children should be able to match and count the objects one-to-one to prove the quantities are the same.

3. After playing this game, place the bags of objects in a corner of the room that children use during free time. Encourage them to play the matching game among themselves.

4. Finally, distribute the **reproducible** on page 13 to the children. Read the directions aloud so that everyone knows what to do.

Name_____ Date_____

Gone Fishing!

Count how many fish are in each picture. Draw the same number of fish.

■ 13 ■

Three, Four, Shut the Door

Objective: Reading numerals from 0 to 10

What You Need:

a copy of the **reproducible** on page 15 for each child

10 large paper clips

crayons

a blank sheet of paper for each child

What You Do:

1. Write the numerals 0 through 10 on the chalkboard and place ten large paper clips on your desk. As you point to a numeral on the chalkboard, ask a volunteer to come to the front of the room and select that number of paper clips. If the answer is correct, that child can select both the next numeral and the next volunteer. Play until each child has had a chance to perform both roles in the activity.

2. Now give a blank sheet of paper to each child and ask children to fold the paper in half from top to bottom. Have each child think of a favorite number and whisper it to you. Write the numeral quite large on the inside of the fold, hidden from view. Then ask the child to draw the same number of objects on the outside of the folded paper. Children then take turns showing their drawings before the class while other children try to guess the secret number.

3. Finally, distribute the **reproducible** on page 15 to the children. Read the directions together before children complete the pages on their own.

Name_____ Date_____

Hide-and-Seek Numbers

Find the numbers from 0 to 10 hidden in the picture. Color them.

■ 15 ■

Five, Six, Pick Up Sticks

Objective: Writing numerals from 1 to 9

What You Need:

copies of the **reproducibles** on pages 17 and 18 for each child

a sheet of paper for each child

counters

crayons

What You Do:

1. Ask children to watch you slowly write the numerals 1 through 9 on the chalkboard. Write carefully and with fairly large movements so children can see how the numerals are made. Select volunteers to write with you on the chalkboard as you repeat the numerals.

2. Next, give each child a piece of paper on which to write the numerals 1 to 9. Encourage good penmanship and display all the papers if possible.

3. Now play a game of lotto. Distribute eight counters and a copy of the **reproducible** game board on page 17 to each child. Read the directions aloud and make sure students understand how to play the game. Have them fill in each box with a number from 1 to 9. Then begin calling numbers randomly until someone wins.

4. For more practice with numerals, distribute copies of the **reproducible** on page 18. Have children complete the sheets on their own after you have read the directions aloud.

Answers for page 18: 4, 1, 6, 5, 2, 5, 3, 9

Name_____ Date_____

Lotto!

Write a different number from 1 to 9 in each space in random order. Listen to your teacher call out a number. Cover it with a counter if you have it. When you get a row up and down, across, or diagonally, call out "Lotto!"

▪ 17 ▪

Name_____ Date_____

A Zooful of Numbers

Write the numerals that match the pictures below the lines. Then read the story and color the picture.

Our class went to the zoo last week. We saw _____ elephants and

_____ baby elephant. We saw _____ giraffes eating from a tall

tree. We saw _____ monkeys playing on Monkey Island. We saw

_____ turtles that were 100 years old. We fed _____ seals.

We got to pet _____ baby goats. We saw _____ penguins.

We hope to go back again.

Answers on page 16

Seven, Eight, Open the Gate

Objective: Learning number order

What You Need:

a copy of the **reproducible** on page 21 for each child

crayons or colored pencils

What You Do:

1. Ask children if they know why the number 4 comes right after the number 3. Explain that each number is one more than the number that comes right before it. Demonstrate this by drawing three cats and a numeral 3 on the chalkboard, along with four cats and a numeral 4. Match the cats one-to-one to show there is one cat left. *Four* is one more than *three*.

2. Now play an oral game of What Number is Next? Say a number aloud and have the children say the next number together. As children progress, you can challenge the class with two- or three-digit numbers.

3. Next, write a number on the chalkboard and choose some students to play another game. The first child writes the number that comes next after yours, the second child writes the number that comes next after that, and so on. When they are done, have children read the numbers in order.

4. To reinforce the idea of number order, distribute copies of the **reproducible** on page 21 to the children. Read the directions aloud before the children complete the connect-the-dots sheets on their own.

5. As a follow-up activity, children might enjoy designing and swapping their own dot-to-dot pictures.

Name_____ Date_____

Missing Pet

A pet is missing. Can you find it? Connect the numbers in order, and the pet will appear! Start at number 1. Color the animal when you find it.

Nine, Ten, an Old Wet Hen

Objective: Learning concepts of greater than and less than

What You Need:

a copy of the **reproducible** on page 23 for each child

a few dozen buttons, coins, or counters

crayons

What You Do:

1. Show the children two unequal piles of buttons. Ask which pile has more buttons. Then have students count the buttons in each pile and record the results on the chalkboard. Ask which number is greater, or more, than the other. Explain that we use the terms *greater than* and *less than* to compare numbers.

2. Repeat the above activity using three, and then four, piles of buttons. Introduce the terms *greatest* and *least*, using the same methods.

3. Finally, write two numerals on the chalkboard and ask children to tell which is the greater and which is the lesser number. Explain that we can use symbols to show which is greater and which is lesser. Write 7 > 3 and 3 < 7 on the chalkboard. Read the number sentences to the children: "*Seven* is greater than *three. Three* is less than *seven*." Write more number sentences and ask the children to read them. Note that the point of the arrow always points to the smaller number.

4. For further practice, distribute copies of the **reproducible** on page 23. Read the directions aloud before children complete the sheets on their own.

Answers for page 23: 37, 51, 58, 31

Name_____ Date_____

What's My Number?

Read what each alien is saying. Color the correct number.

My number is < 55. It is > 28. What's my number?		19 37 61
My number is < 75. It is > 49. What's my number?		51 30 92
My number is > 38. It is < 88. What's my number?		38 98 58
My number is > 15. It is < 46. What's my number?		31 78 49

Make your own number puzzle.

My number is

It is

What's my number?   ____   ____   ____

Answers on page 22

■ 23 ■

It All Adds Up

Objective: Understanding addition

What You Need:

copies of the **reproducibles** on pages 26 and 27 for each child

a copy of the **reproducible** on page 25 for each group of 4 children

tagboard or posterboard

a paper fastener (brad) for each spinner

crayons

What You Do:

1. Tell the class that addition is the act of putting two or more sets together. Ask a volunteer to pick two numbers under 10 for you to add. Write the numbers on the chalkboard as an addition problem. Then assemble two groups of students, each corresponding in number to one of the numbers on the board. Have a volunteer count the total number of students. Write the number as the answer to the addition problem. Tell children that the answer to an addition problem is called the *sum*.

2. Now prepare spinners for the Make-a-Face Game by following directions on the **reproducible** on page 25. Then distribute a copy of the **reproducible** on page 26 to each child. Read the directions aloud until children understand the game. Divide the class into groups of four and have them play the game. The first child to draw a complete face is the winner.

3. For another fun activity to practice addition, distribute copies of the **reproducible** on page 27. Read the directions aloud before children complete the pages.

Answer for page 27: All the problems that total 9 form a picture of an orange, long-haired dog.

Make-a-Face Spinner

Color the spinner. Then paste the spinner and the pointer onto tagboard or posterboard and cut them out. Attach the pointer to the spinner base, using a paper brad. Be sure the pointer spins freely. Use the spinner to play the Make-a-Face Game on page 26.

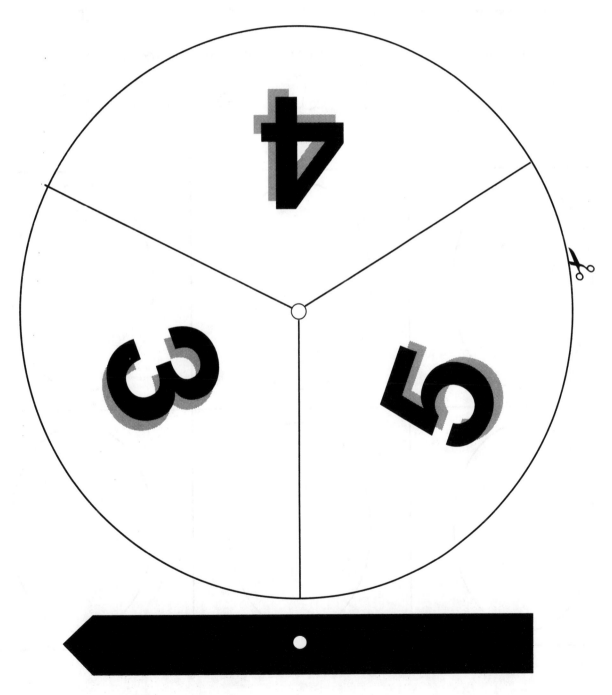

Addition

Name_____ Date_____

Make-a-Face Game

1. Take turns spinning the spinner two times.

2. Find the sum of the two numbers the arrow points to.

3. Draw the correct part of the face.

If the sum is:	6	7	8	9	10
Draw this part:	eyes	nose	mouth	ears	hair

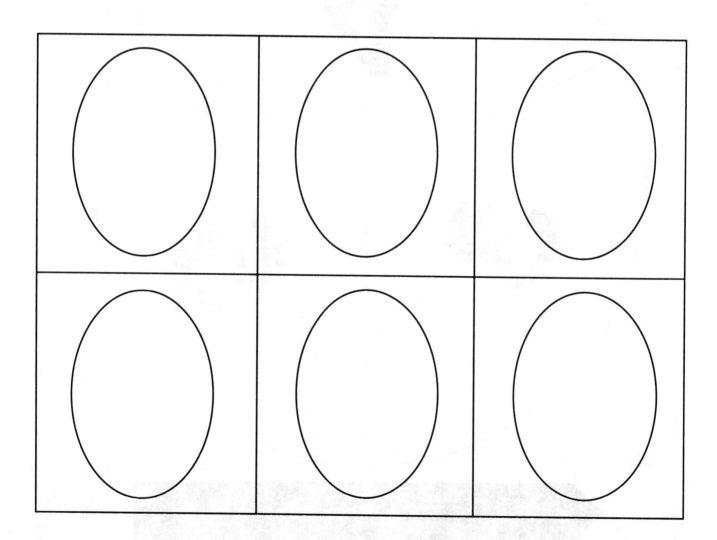

Name_____ Date_____

What Am I?

Add the numbers. Find each sum and the color it matches. Color the spaces to find the animal.

If the sum is:	3	4	5	6	7	8	9	10
Color the space:	red	blue	green	pink	yellow	brown	orange	black

$2 + 6 =$

$\begin{array}{r} 5 \\ +\,1 \\ \hline \end{array}$

$\begin{array}{r} 2 \\ +\,2 \\ \hline \end{array}$

$2 + 7 =$

$\begin{array}{r} 1 \\ +\,8 \\ \hline \end{array}$

$\begin{array}{r} 5 \\ +\,5 \\ \hline \end{array}$

$\begin{array}{r} 5 \\ +\,3 \\ \hline \end{array}$

$\begin{array}{r} 1 \\ +\,2 \\ \hline \end{array}$

$\begin{array}{r} 5 \\ +\,4 \\ \hline \end{array}$

$4 + 1 =$

$\begin{array}{r} 3 \\ +\,2 \\ \hline \end{array}$

$4 + 5 =$

$\begin{array}{r} 7 \\ +\,2 \\ \hline \end{array}$

$\begin{array}{r} 6 \\ +\,3 \\ \hline \end{array}$

$\begin{array}{r} 5 \\ +\,3 \\ \hline \end{array}$

$\begin{array}{r} 5 \\ +\,2 \\ \hline \end{array}$

$\begin{array}{r} 3 \\ +\,6 \\ \hline \end{array}$

$\begin{array}{r} 4 \\ +\,4 \\ \hline \end{array}$

$\begin{array}{r} 3 \\ +\,4 \\ \hline \end{array}$

$3 + 3 =$

$\begin{array}{r} 8 \\ +\,1 \\ \hline \end{array}$

$2 + 1 =$

$7 + 1 =$

$\begin{array}{r} 3 \\ +\,1 \\ \hline \end{array}$

Answer on page 24

▪ 27 ▪

Puttin' It All Together

Objective: Understanding addition

8

What You Need:

a copy of the **reproducible** on page 29 for each child

3-4 copies of the **reproducibles** on pages 30 and 31

a yardstick

buttons or counters

tagboard or cardboard

scissors

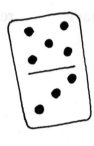

What You Do:

1. Gather the children around your desk or a large table. Lay down a yardstick to represent a number line. Tell the class that you want to add 5 plus 7. Ask one of the children to put a button or counter on the number 5 on the yardstick. Then ask another child to move the counter seven spaces ahead on the yardstick, counting out loud from 1 to 7 as the counter is moved. The counter will now be on the number 12. Point out that 5 and 7 add up to 12. Give pairs of children other sums to add up on the yardstick.

2. Distribute copies of the **reproducible** on page 29 to the children. Read the directions aloud before they complete the pages individually.

3. For another game, paste copies of the **reproducibles** on pages 30 and 31 on tagboard or posterboard and cut apart the dominoes. Have children find all the dominoes whose dots add up to 2, 3, 4, 5, etc. Save the dominoes to use later for subtraction.

Answers for page 29: 10 box—vertical: 5+5, 3+7, 1+9, 4+6; horizontal: 2+8   14 box—vertical: 6+8, 9+5, 10+4, 7+7; horizontal: 8+6   12 box—vertical: 3+9, 7+5, 6+6; horizontal: 9+3, 8+4
11 box—vertical: 5+6, 8+3; horizontal: 7+4, 8+3, 6+5

Name_____ Date_____

Find the Hidden Pairs

Find two numbers next to each other that add up to the number shown.
Circle these pairs. Pairs can go up and down or across. Two examples are
circled for you in the first box.

2 8 3 6 8 4 1 0 1 5 3 6 6 3 9 7 4 9 5 7 2 2 4 7 5 2 9 0 9 2 Find 5 number pairs that add up to 10.	6 2 9 1 7 6 8 1 5 4 9 3 7 5 10 3 7 9 3 2 4 8 7 6 8 6 0 4 8 1 Find 5 number pairs that add up to 14.
1 9 7 1 5 6 2 6 9 3 2 6 3 5 1 2 8 0 9 4 7 0 7 1 8 4 0 9 5 3 Find 5 number pairs that add up to 12.	5 1 9 5 7 4 6 4 6 7 2 5 1 9 9 1 2 0 8 3 6 3 4 8 0 7 1 6 5 3 Find 5 number pairs that add up to 11.

Answers on page 28

Dominoes

Dominoes

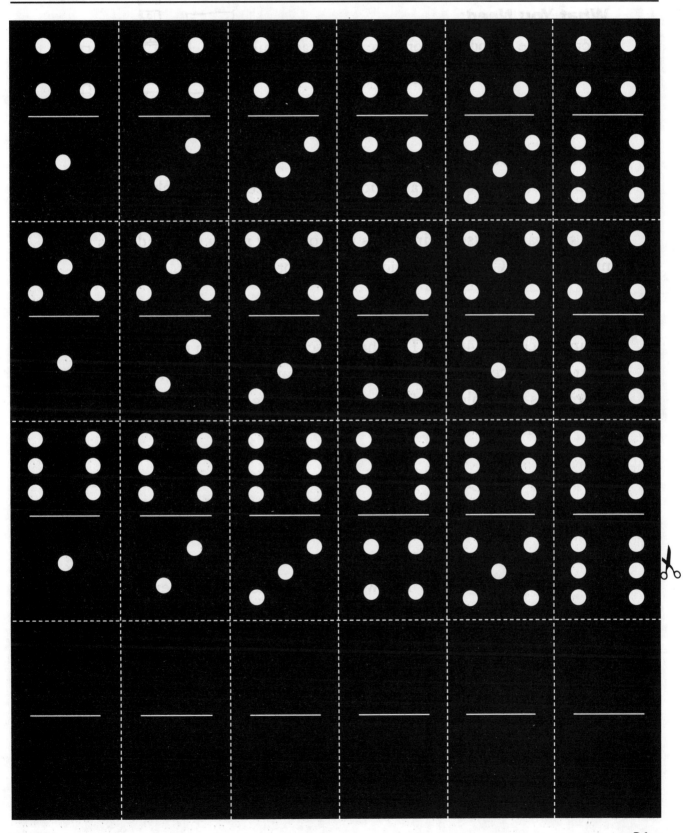

A Whole Lot More

Objective: Understanding two-digit addition

What You Need:

a copy of the **reproducible** on page 33 for each child

10 ones-place value blocks per pair of children

10 tens-place value blocks per pair of children

What You Do:

1. Distribute ten ones-place and ten tens-place value blocks to each pair of children. Then write a two-digit number on the chalkboard. Ask the pairs to use their blocks to show how many tens and ones the number has. Continue the activity with other numbers.

2. Next, write an addition problem using only tens on the chalkboard, for instance, 30 + 40 = ? The children can model each number with their tens-place blocks and then find the sum by adding the total number of tens-place blocks. Point out that adding tens is just like adding ones, except it is done in the tens place.

3. Now write the problem 52 + 11 in vertical form on the board. Ask the children which blocks they will need to model this problem. (5 tens and 2 ones plus 1 ten and 1 one.) Point out that the ones of one number are written exactly over the ones of the other number, and the same is true for the tens. Allow them to model the problem and find the answer.

4. Finally, distribute copies of the **reproducible** on page 33 to the children. Read the directions aloud before the students complete the pages on their own.

Answer for page 33: 53 + 45 = 98

Name_____ Date_____

The King's Secret Number

King Randolff the Fifth has a treasure box full of gold. Anyone who finds his secret number can have half of the gold. King Randolff will give only these clues:

1. The number is the sum of two of the numbers below.

2. The number is larger than 91.

Find King Randolff's secret number and win half of the gold! Which numbers below can you add to get more than 91? Find out and win the gold!

11   53   22   34   21   14   45   32   24   33

What is King Randolff's secret number? _____

Answer on page 32

Left Overs

Objective: Understanding simple subtraction

What You Need:

a copy of the **reproducible** on page 35 for each child

9 counters for each pair of children
(buttons, pennies, or beans)

What You Do:

1. Show the children nine counters. Ask them to count and tell you how many counters there are. Now have them close their eyes as you remove a few counters. When they open their eyes, ask how many counters have been taken away and how many are left. On the chalkboard, write the subtraction fact you have just demonstrated (for example, 9-2=7). Continue the activity with different pairs of students. Ask one student to take away counters, while the other student counts the objects remaining and writes the subtraction problem on the board.

2. For more practice in subtraction, distribute the **reproducible** on page 35 to the children. Read the directions aloud before the students work on the sheets individually.

Answers for page 35: 6, 5, 4, 7, 5

Name_____ Date_____

Henrietta Munch

Henrietta Munch was not invited to the Piggies' Picnic. She came anyway. She ate most of the food. How much did she eat?

Prunella Piggy brought 8 hot dogs.   These are left:

Henrietta ate _____ hot dogs.

Percy Piggy brought 9 hamburgers.   These are left:

Henrietta ate _____ hamburgers.

Pamela Piggy brought 5 pizzas.   This is left:

Henrietta ate _____ pizzas.

Potsy Piggy brought 9 sandwiches.   These are left:

Henrietta ate _____ sandwiches.

Patsy Piggy brought 6 ice-cream cones.   This is left:

Henrietta ate _____ ice-cream cones.

Answers on page 34

■ ■

What's Left?

Objective: Understanding subtraction

What You Need:

a copy of the **reproducible** on page 37 for each child

small slips of paper

a box with slot in top

stickers

a yardstick

counters

crayons

$$10$$
$$-\ 4$$
$$\overline{6}$$

What You Do:

1. Every day, write a different subtraction problem on a piece of paper and post it on the bulletin board. Have each child write his or her name and the answer to the problem on a slip of paper and place the paper in a box. At the end of the day, check the answers and place a sticker next to the name of each student whose answer is correct.

2. For more practice with subtraction, lay a yardstick on a surface where the class can see it. Place a counter on the number 10. Then tell children you want to take away, or subtract, 4 from 10. Ask a volunteer to move the counter back four spaces on the yardstick, counting out loud from 1 to 4. Students have just shown that 10-4=6. Tell them that the answer to a subtraction problem is called the *difference*.

3. To make a game out of subtraction, distribute copies of the **reproducible** on 37. Read the directions aloud and let children solve the maze puzzles on their own.

Answers for page 37: Problems with differences of 9: 14-5, 10-1, 16-7, 13-4, 11-2, 18-9, 15-6, 12-3, 17-8

Name_____ Date_____

The Lost Pony

Tonto the Pony is lost. He wants to go back to his barn. Can you help him find his way?

Find all the differences. Color the facts that have a difference of 9 to make a path for Tonto.

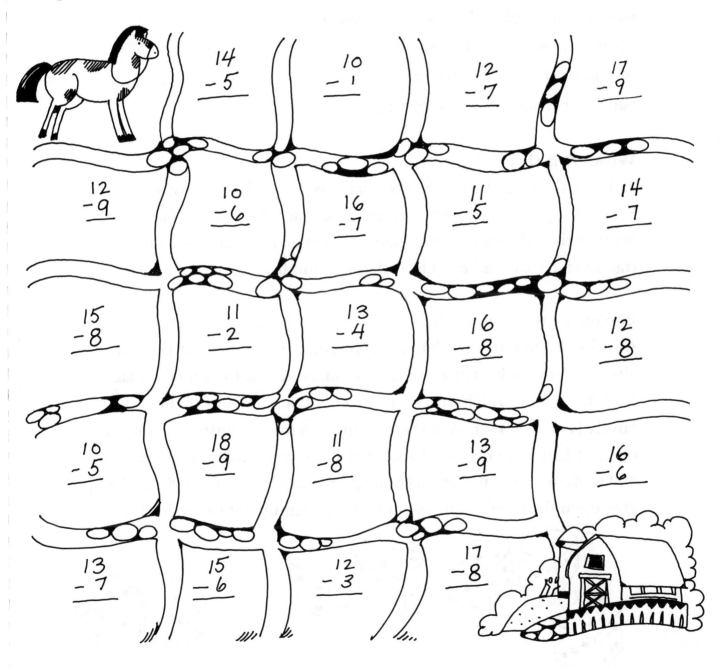

Just the Facts

Objective: Understanding fact families

What You Need:

6-8 copies of the game board **reproducibles** on pages 40 and 41

6-8 copies of the playing cards **reproducible** on page 42

a copy of the **reproducible** on page 43 for each child

posterboard or tagboard to make 6-8 game boards

a pair of scissors for each group to share

several dice for children to share

buttons or counters to use as playing pieces

What You Do:

1. Write these math facts on the chalkboard: 3 + 5 = 8; 5 + 3 = 8; 8 - 5 = 3; 8 - 3 = 5. Explain that these four facts form a *fact family* because they all use the same numbers and no more addition or subtraction facts can be be made with these numbers.

2. Now write three members of another fact family on the board. Ask the children to tell what fact is missing. Point out that there are always four members of a fact family, unless the fact is a doubles fact such as 4 + 4, in which case there are only two members of the fact family (4+4=8; 8-4=4). Ask three volunteers to each write a member of one fact family on the board and then ask another volunteer to come up and write the missing fact to complete the family. If students need help, give them the numbers to use in their fact family (for example, 2, 7, 9).

3. To review addition and subtraction facts, make several game boards by pasting copies of the two halves of the Deep Space Game Board (**reproducibles**, pages 40 and 41) together on tagboard and cutting them out. Organize the class into groups of four or fewer players. Give each group a Deep Space Game Board and Deep Space Playing Cards (**reproducible**, page 42) to cut apart before playing. Read the following directions aloud so everyone knows what to do.

DIRECTIONS:

1. Cut out the addition and subtraction playing cards and put them face down in the middle of the board.

2. Two, three, or four people can play this game. Each player puts a marker on a different "Start" box. Players may start off in any direction.

3. Each player takes a turn picking a math-problem card and giving the answer out loud. The player moves 3 steps ahead toward one of the docks if the group agrees that the answer is right or 1 space back if the answer is wrong. Players put used cards in another pile.

4. The first person to dock or get closest to the dock by the time the cards are gone wins the game.

---

4. For more practice with subtraction, organize the class into the same number of groups as you have dice. Distribute copies of the **reproducible** on page 43 to the children and read the directions aloud. Tell the groups to toss their dice. Then have them subtract the number that comes up on the die from the number indicated above each picture. Children then draw the "creature feature" found under the number that represents the difference.

Deep Space Game Board

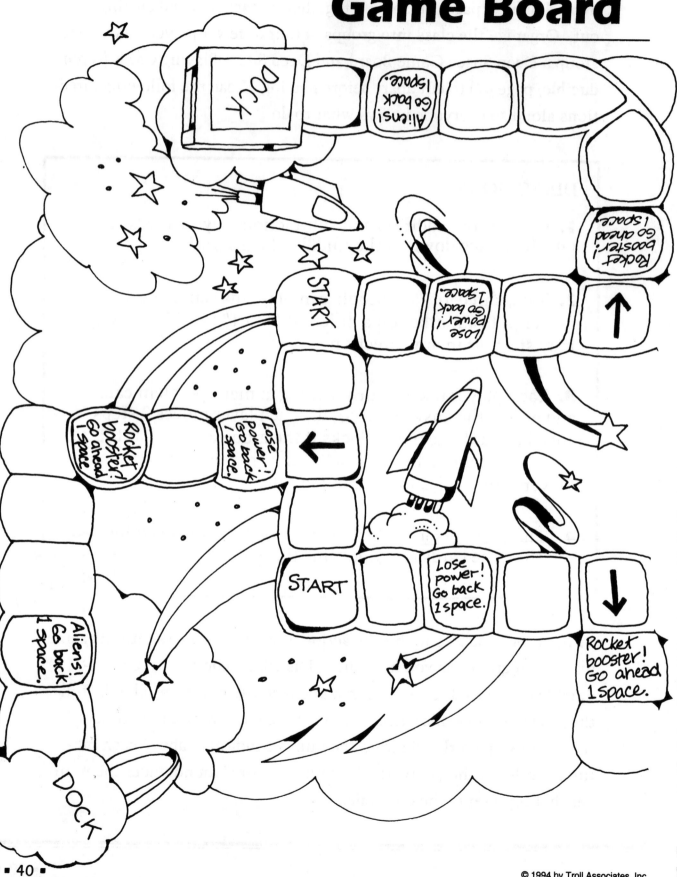

Deep Space Playing Cards

9 + 8	8 + 7	9 + 9	6 + 7	7 + 9	5 + 4
6 + 8	8 + 5	4 + 7	3 + 7	6 + 6	2 + 9
18 - 9	17 - 8	16 - 7	14 - 6	15 - 7	15 - 9
13 - 6	12 - 5	11 - 6	10 - 4	13 - 8	9 - 4

Subtraction

Name_____ Date_____

Creature Features

Can you draw a funny creature? Toss the die. Subtract the number of dots on the die from the number above each creature. Draw the feature shown under the number that is the same as your answer.

If your answer is:	1	2	3	4	5	6	7	8
Draw this part:	eyes	nose	mouth	ears	hair	teeth	tail	feet

Subtract from 8.

Subtract from 7.

Subtract from 9.

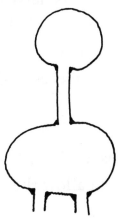

Make your own game.

Sharing a New Idea

Objective: Understanding equal parts

What You Need:

a copy of the **reproducible** on page 45
   for each child

2 apples

a knife (for teacher use only)

2 paper circles 6" in diameter

scissors

crayons

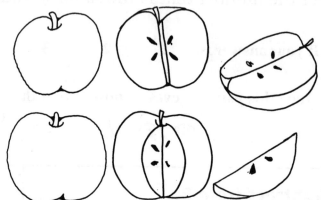

What You Do:

1. Cut two apples, one in halves, the other in two unequal pieces. Ask children to show which pieces are equal. Say that two equal parts that make a whole are called *halves*. Does the other apple show two halves? (No, because the two pieces are not equal.) Now cut each half in two equal pieces. Explain that four equal parts that make a whole are called *fourths* or *quarters*.

2. Now show two paper circles, one with a dotted line dividing it into halves, the other with a dotted line dividing it into two unequal pieces that are very close to being equal. Ask which circle shows halves. Have volunteers cut carefully along the dotted lines of both circles and place the parts on top of one another. The circle that showed halves should have pieces that match exactly, while the other pieces will be close, but not exact.

3. Finally, distribute copies of the **reproducible** on page 45 to each child. Read the directions together as a class and then allow the children to complete the work on their own.

Name_____ Date_____

Are They Equal?

Which of these figures show equal parts? Circle them.

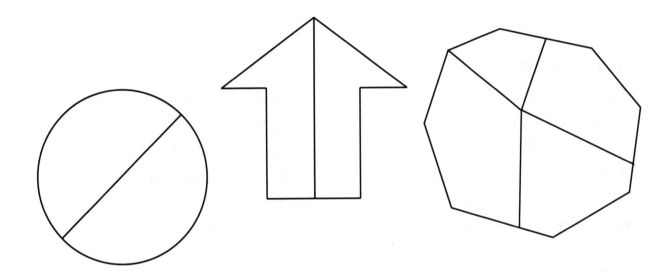

Color all the parts of Square 1 blue. Color all the parts of Square 2 red.
Cut out the squares and their parts. Which square shows equal parts?

Square 1   **Square 2**

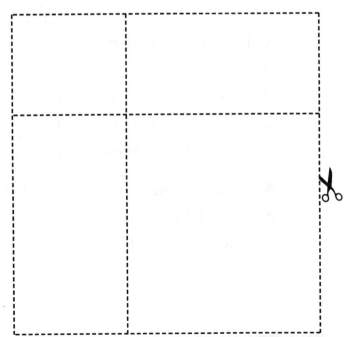

■ 45 ■

Just a Fraction

Objective: Understanding fractions

What You Need:

a copy of the **reproducible** on page 47 for each child
crayons

What You Do:

1. Draw a square on the chalkboard and a dotted line dividing it in half. Color one of the halves. Ask what the filled-in part is called. Children should be able to name it *one-half*. Then ask if they know how to write *one-half* in numbers. Write the fraction. Tell children that the 2 on the bottom shows that the square is divided into two equal parts. The 1 on the top shows that only one of the two parts is filled in.

2. Repeat the exercise for $\frac{1}{3}$ and $\frac{1}{4}$. Vary the exercise by using circles and rectangles. Each time, ask children what each number in the fraction means.

3. Afterward, go on a fraction hunt around the school. Ask the children to find things that are divided into equal pieces. For instance, a ruler will show equal markings and a clock is divided into equal sections. Perhaps you can find a bookcase with equal shelves, equal panes in a large window, or equal tiles on the floor. Each time, ask how many equal parts there are and what one part is called.

4. For more fun with fractions, distribute copies of the **reproducible** on page 47. Read the directions together and then have children complete the sheets individually.

Fractions

Name_____ Date_____

Have Some Pizza

Mrs. Pepper wants to try samples from different pizzas.
Draw lines to divide into equal pieces. Color the
number of pieces that Mrs. Pepper wants to try.

Pepperoni and Onion $\frac{1}{2}$

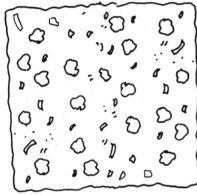

Sausage and Pepper $\frac{1}{3}$

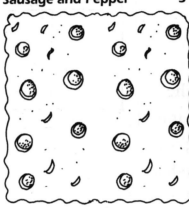

Plain $\frac{1}{8}$

Garlic, Onion, and Sausage $\frac{3}{4}$

Spinach and Squash 0

Anchovies and Bacon $\frac{4}{8}$

Mushroom, Pepper, and Sausage $\frac{1}{4}$

Garlic and Liver $\frac{2}{3}$

The Kitchen Sink $\frac{7}{8}$

■ 47 ■

What's Missing Here?

Objective: Writing fractions

What You Need:

a copy of the **reproducible** on
page 49 for each child

a sheet of construction paper

square stick-on notes

What You Do:

1. Draw a rectangle on the
chalkboard and divide it into
eighths. Color in one eighth.
Ask the children to tell what
part is colored. Then ask a vol-
unteer to write the fraction on the board. Now shade in another eighth
of the rectangle and ask a volunteer to write the new fraction shown by
the colored part. Continue until the entire rectangle is colored in.

2. Next, cover a sheet of construction paper with stick-on notes, and
show it to the children. Ask how many notes there are. Write that
number on the board. After the children close their eyes, remove one
or more stick-on notes from the arrangement. Tell them to open their
eyes and tell how many notes are missing. Write that number above
the total number of notes that were on the sheet to make a fraction.
Repeat the activity with different fractions.

3. Finally, distribute copies of the **reproducible** on page 49. Read the
directions together to make sure students understand what to do.
Then allow them to complete the pages on their own.

Answers for page 49: 1. 5/20 (1/4) 2. 3/8 3. 7/12 4. 8/9 5. 12/24 (1/2) 6. 1/12

Fractions

Name_____ Date_____

Hungry Halburth

Hungry Halburth got into the bakery. He tried at least one bite of every cake. Write the fraction that shows how much of each cake is missing. The first example is done for you.

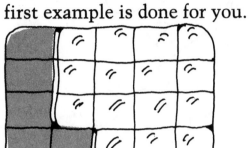

1. chocolate $\dfrac{5}{20}$ **2.** lemon _____

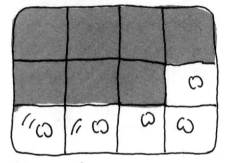
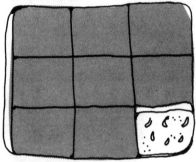

3. strawberry _____   **4.** vanilla _____

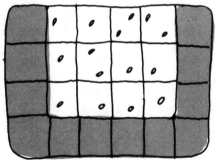
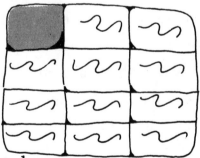

5. raisin _____   **6.** banana _____

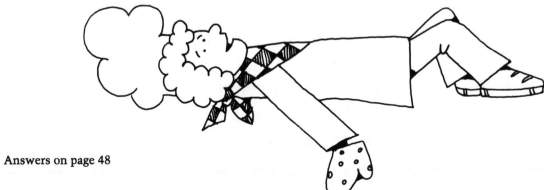

Answers on page 48

© 1994 by Troll Associates, Inc. ■ 49 ■

Shape Up!

Objective: Identifying two-dimensional shapes

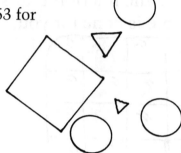

What You Need:

copies of the **reproducibles** on pages 51, 52, and 53 for
 each child

shape flashcards or blocks if available

4-6 pairs of scissors for children to share

crayons

What You Do:

1. Using flashcards or blocks, ask children to identify a
variety of shapes—circles, squares, triangles, and rectangles. Then organize a game of I Spy with the class.
Name a shape and have the children point to an object
in the classroom that has the same basic shape.

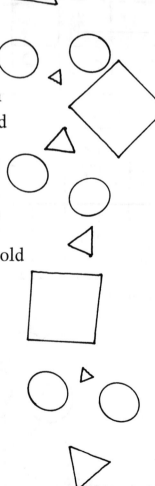

2. Now play a game of Shape Lotto. Give one copy each
of the **reproducible** cards and game board on pages 51 and
52 to each child. Have each child cut apart the shape
cards on page 51, mix them up, and put them in a pile;
then pick one shape at a time and copy it in one of the
boxes on page 52. To play the game, cut apart a sheet of
Lotto cards for yourself, mix them up, choose one, and hold
it up for the class to see. Each child places his or her
matching shape card on the correct space on the game
board. The first to get four shape cards in a row up and
down, across, or diagonally wins the game.

3. For more practice with shapes, distribute copies of
the **reproducible** on page 53. Read the directions aloud.
Then let children find the shapes on their own.

Shape Lotto Cards

Shape Lotto Game Board

Draw a shape in each empty space. Then play a game of Shape Lotto. Look at the shape cards your teacher holds up. Cover the shape with a marker. Call out "Lotto!" if you fill a row up and down, across, or diagonally.

Name_____ Date_____ ▪ 53 ▪

Find the Shapes

Find the circles, squares, rectangles, and triangles in the picture. Color each shape a different color.

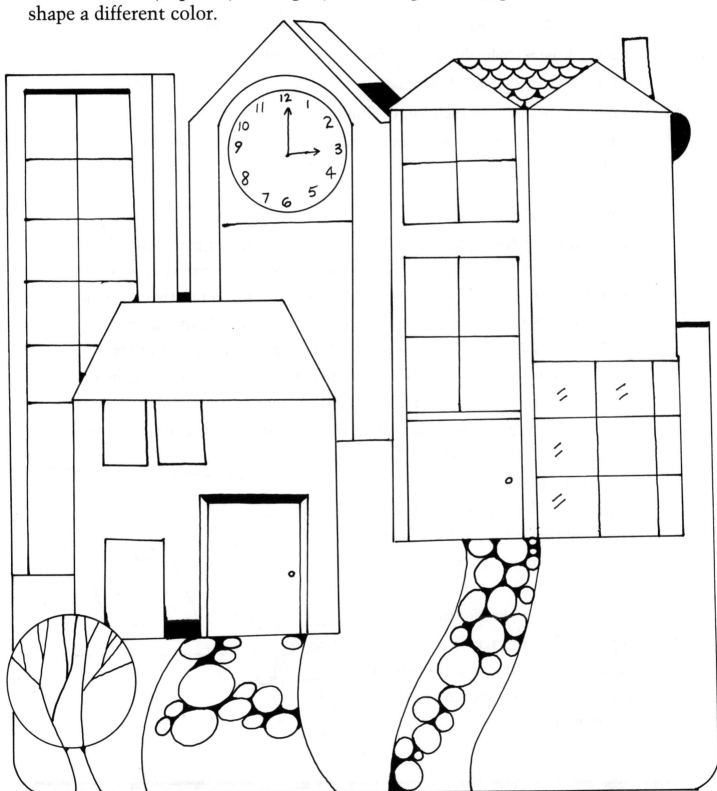

▪ 53 ▪

Which Side of the Fence?

Objective: Understanding the concepts of inside and outside

What You Need:

a copy of the **reproducible** on page 55 for each pair of children

a copy of the **reproducible** on page 56 for each child

30 3" x 5" index cards: 10 marked *inside*, 10 *outside*, and 10 *take away*

number cube or die for each pair of children

a dozen plastic counters of one color and a dozen of another color for each pair of children

What You Do:

1. Review the concepts of *inside* and *outside*. Then organize the children into pairs to play the Inside, Outside game. Give each pair of children a copy of the **reproducible** on page 55 and a dozen plastic counters apiece in separate colors. Taking turns, the children choose an index card and toss the number cube or die. If the child chooses an index card that says *inside* and rolls a 4 on the cube or die, for example, he or she places four counters inside the circle. Counters go outside the circle if an *outside* card is drawn. A *take away* card means the child can remove any counters—the child's or the opponent's—from any place on the paper. The player to get exactly five counters inside and five counters outside the circle wins.

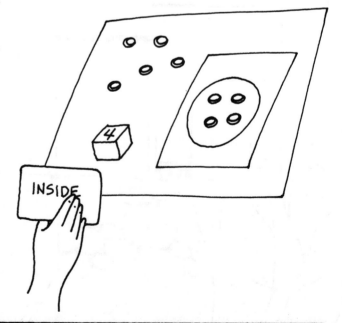

2. Distribute copies of the **reproducible** on page 56 to the class. Go over the directions before the children complete the pages individually.

Inside, Outside

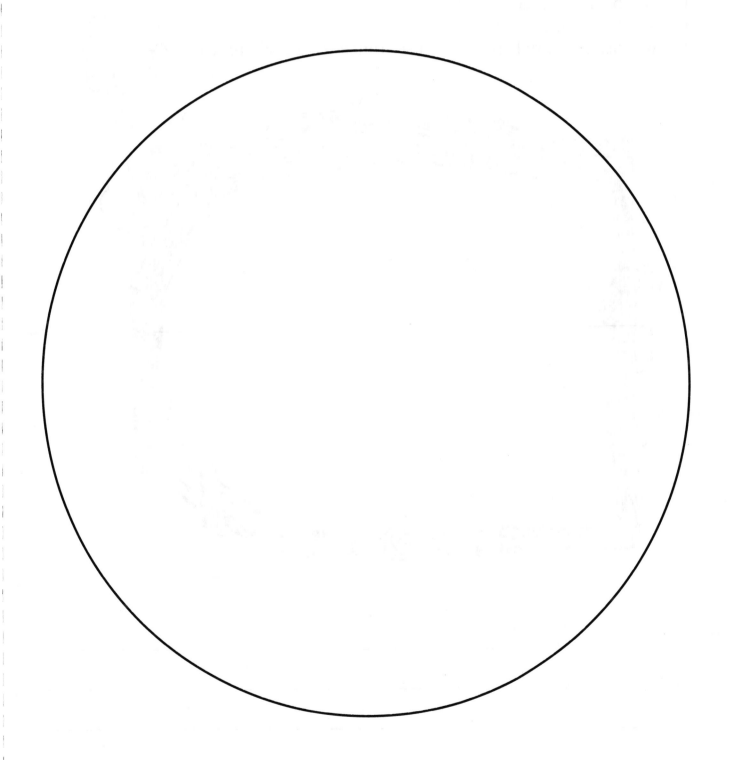

Inside and Outside

Name_____ Date_____

Where Are They?

Draw 4 elephants inside the fence.
Draw 3 bears outside the fence.
Draw 2 birds on the fence.
Draw 1 other animal and write a sentence to tell where it is.

_____

_____

_____

_____

Follow Me

Objective: Giving and following directions

What You Need:

a copy of the **reproducible** on page 59 for each child

a crayon or colored marker for each child

What You Do:

1. Discuss the importance of giving good directions and of listening carefully to directions. Have the children practice giving and following directions by playing a simple game of Simon Says. Give a series of specific directions for players to follow, for example: "Simon says raise your right hand, touch your left toe, and turn around." After a few rounds, encourage a volunteer to give a similar series of directions for the other children to follow.

2. Now have pairs of children work together to write directions from the classroom to another room in the school building. They can then trade papers and try to follow each other's directions.

3. Finally, organize the children into pairs. Give each child a copy of the **reproducible** on page 59. Explain that one child draws dots in any location on his or her paper and then gives directions for the other child to follow on his or her own paper to figure out the location of the dots. Tell the children to keep the whereabouts of their dots out of view from each other until their partners figure out where the dots are. Children then switch roles.

Follow the Dots

Draw three dots on this map. Then give your partner directions to follow on his or her map to figure out where the dots are.

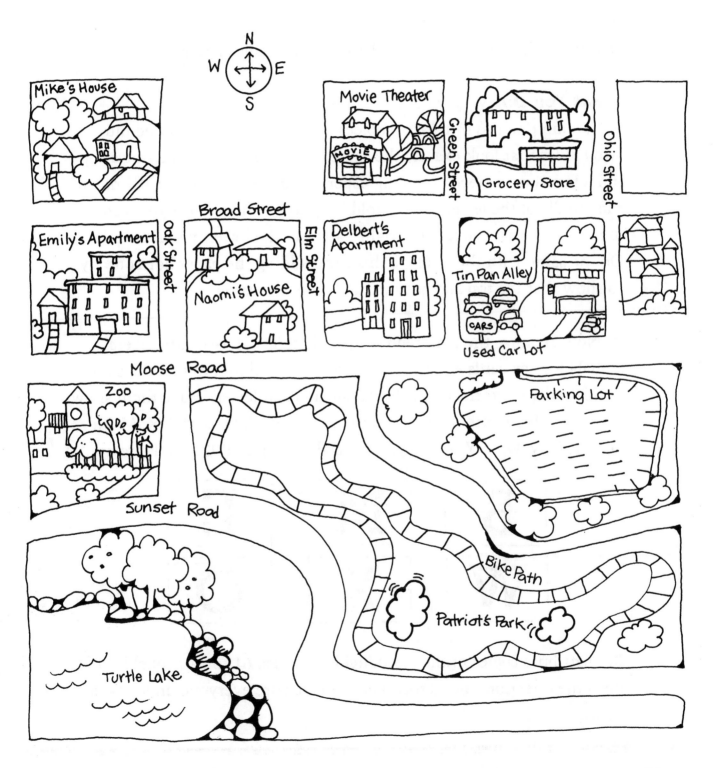

Fold It!

Objective: Understanding symmetry

What You Need:

a copy of the **reproducible** on page 61 for each pair of children

tracing paper

26 index cards with a large capital letter in the middle of each one

What You Do:

1. Explain that a *symmetrical* object is one that can be divided into two halves that look exactly the same. Demonstrate by drawing a capital letter *A* on a piece of tracing paper. Fold the paper vertically down the middle of the letter. Then hold it up to a window or light so children can see that the left and right halves of the letter match exactly. Do the same with the letter *E*, this time folding the paper horizontally to show that the top and bottom halves are the same.

2. Now organize the children into small groups. Distribute several alphabet index cards to each group. Ask the children to fold the cards horizontally or vertically in the middle of each letter. Have them show the class which letters are symmetrical. (A, B, C, D, E, H, I, K, M, N, O, S, T, U, V, W, X, Y, Z are symmetrical; F, G, J, L, P, Q, and R are not.)

3. Distribute copies of the **reproducible** on page 61 to pairs of children. Read the directions aloud together to make sure everyone understands them.

Names_____ Date_____

Halvsies

Draw half of a shape on one side of the dotted line. Then let your partner draw the other half to make it symmetrical. Trade places and do it again.

Mirror, Mirror

Objective: Recognizing mirror images

What You Need:

a copy of the **reproducible** on page 63 for each child

a copy of the mirror sentence below for each child

4-6 small mirrors for the class to share

What You Do:

1. Demonstrate a mirror image for the class. Whisper to a volunteer to slowly scratch her head with her right hand, hop twice on her left foot, and clap three times. Face the volunteer and perform all the movements at the same time, but in a mirror image. That is, duplicate the same actions with your left hand and right foot. Ask the class to tell what was the same about your movements (the scratching, hopping, and clapping), and what was different (right versus left). Allow the children to pair off and try this exercise. First, designate one partner as the "mirror" and then have them switch roles.

2. Next, distribute copies of the mirror sentence below to each child.

My mother's name is Fred.

Explain to the children that they will be learning a secret code. Distribute mirrors to the children and ask them to figure out the mirror sentence before passing the mirror on to children sitting nearby.

3. Distribute copies of the **reproducible** on page 63. Allow children plenty of time to match the mirror images.

Mirror, Mirror on the Wall

Cut out the shapes. Put them face to face. See if they match.

All in a Row

What You Need:

copies of the **reproducibles** on pages 65, 66, and 67 for each child

crayons

several pairs of scissors for children to share

What You Do:

1. Tell the children they are going to look for patterns and make some on their own. Explain that a pattern is a repeated arrangement of objects, details, or pictures. Invite children to look for any patterns in the class. Some children might notice patterned tiles on the floor or walls or someone's polka dot socks and striped shirt.

2. Now distribute copies of the **reproducible** on page 65. Ask children to color the shapes and cut out the tiles. Then have the children work in groups of four to make a pattern with the shapes. Groups can then try to copy each other's patterns.

3. For more fun with patterns, distribute copies of the **reproducible** on page 66. Read the directions aloud before children complete the pages on their own.

4. Finally, distribute copies of the **reproducible** on page 67 to the children. Have children discuss different kinds of patterns they could color on their quilts. Hang the finished quilts on a "clothesline" in the classroom.

Shape Pattern Tiles

Color the shapes and cut out the boxes. Then arrange the boxes into your own patterns.

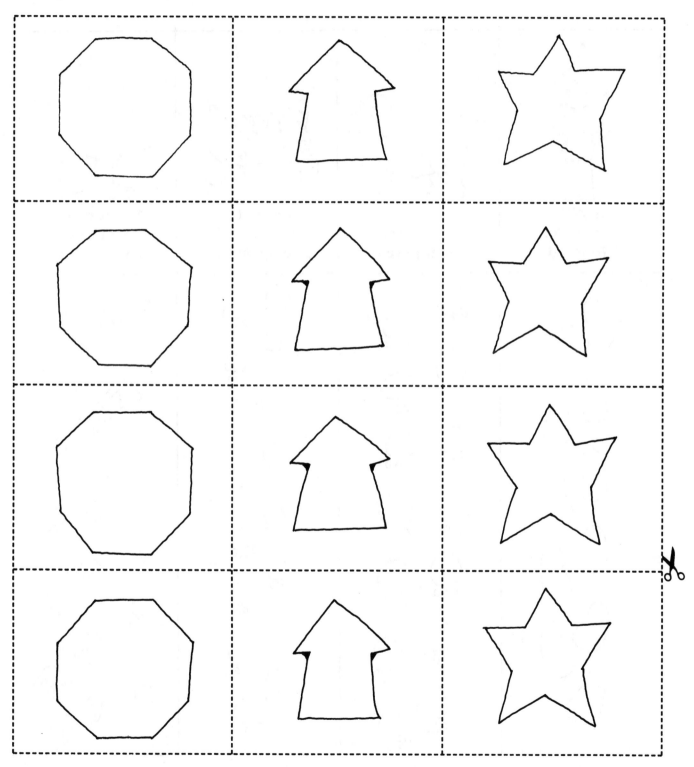

Name_____ Date_____

Footprint Patterns

Somebody spilled colored paints, and everyone walked in the splatters. Color the patterns the footprints would make.

1	2	3	4
1 foot blue 1 foot red	2 feet green 2 feet purple	1 foot red 1 foot blue 2 feet yellow	1 foot green 1 foot purple 1 foot orange

Name_____ Date_____

Sleeping Kitten

Make a pattern on the quilt by coloring the squares different colors. For example, you could make a checkerboard pattern with two different colors.

Get a Head

Objective: *Comparing lengths*

What You Need:

a copy of the **reproducible** on page 69 for each child

pencils of different lengths

24" strips of paper, string, or yarn

scissors

What To Do:

1. Review the concepts of longer and shorter by having children compare pencils of different lengths.

2. Now organize the class into pairs. Give each child a strip of paper, string, or yarn 24" long. Have the partners measure the circumference of each other's heads, using the strips. Partners can mark the strips and then cut them to the exact sizes. Tell children to write their names on their strips and color them their favorite colors. Display the strips on the bulletin board to show the head sizes of students in the class.

3. For more practice, distribute copies of the **reproducible** on page 69 to the class and read the directions aloud before children complete the sheets on their own. Note that the answers will vary, depending on the length of the pencils used to make comparisons.

Name_____ Date_____

Longer and Shorter Snakes

Which snakes are longer than your pencil? Color them green. Which snakes are shorter than your pencil? Color them purple.

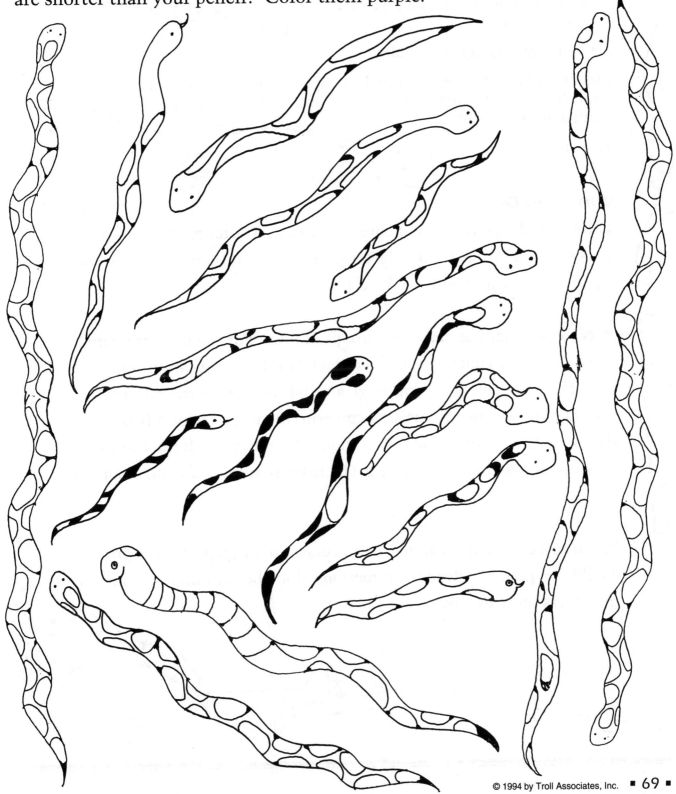

■ 69 ■

Measure for Measure

Objective: Measuring inches

What You Need:

a copy of the **reproducible** on page 71
  for each child

a ruler for each group of 4 children

1 index card per child, each labeled with a measurement that can be found
  on whatever size rulers students are using. Label each card with a
  different measurement.

a paper bag

What You Do:

1. Review the divisions of inches on a ruler. Ask for pairs of volunteers to measure classroom objects in inches with their own rulers and report the measurements to the class.

2. Now organize the class into groups of four. Put the measurement index cards in a paper bag and have each child select a card from the bag. Then instruct the teams to go around the classroom and find objects that have nearly the same measurements as the numbers shown on their cards. The teams should keep lists of all the things they find for each measurement. The team that finds the most objects wins.

3. For more fun with measurements, distribute copies of the **reproducible** on page 71. Read the directions aloud before children complete the sheets individually.

Name_____ Date_____

Measure Up!

You can measure yourself and things in your world with a ruler. Write the measurements below.

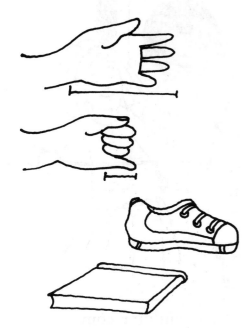

My hand is _____ long.

My little finger is _____ long.

My shoe is _____ long.

My math book is _____ long.

My pencil is _____ long.

From my wrist to my elbow

is _____ long.

From my knee to the floor

is _____ long.

If I had a pet fish, it would

be_____ long.

Much Longer

Objective: Measuring yards

What You Need:

a copy of the **reproducible** on page 73 for each child

a yardstick

a roll-out style tape measure

What You Do:

1. Examine a yardstick with the children. What are the smaller units that make up this big unit? (feet and inches) How many of these smaller units are in a yard? (3 feet, 36 inches)

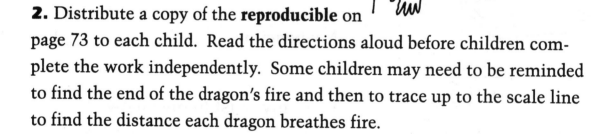

2. Distribute a copy of the **reproducible** on page 73 to each child. Read the directions aloud before children complete the work independently. Some children may need to be reminded to find the end of the dragon's fire and then to trace up to the scale line to find the distance each dragon breathes fire.

3. Extend the "Dragon Fire" exercise by playing an estimation game. After children have completed the **reproducible**, remind them that Petunia could breathe fire 4 yards. Ask a volunteer to show what he or she thinks is about 4 yards from a wall. Then have two other volunteers use a tape measure or a yardstick to measure the actual distance. How close was the estimate? Repeat the activity with new volunteers and new distances.

Answers for page 73: Petunia = 4, Daisy = 2, Snap = 5, Rosebud = 3. Snap breathes fire the farthest.

Name_____ Date_____

Dragon's Fire

Read the chart. Then answer the questions below.

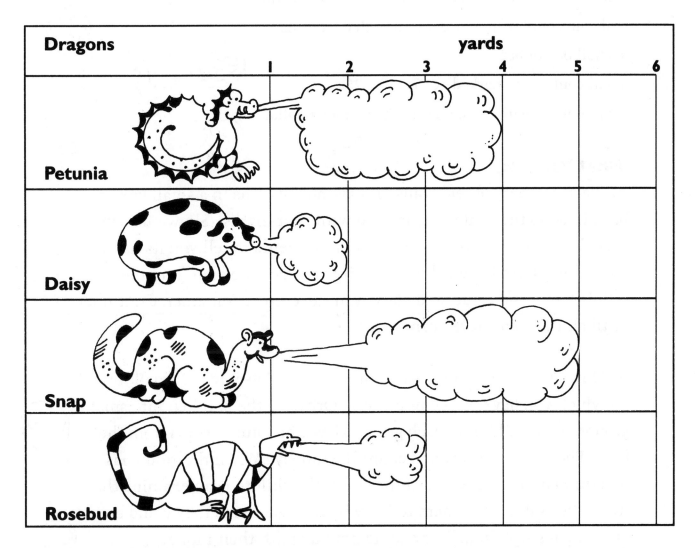

How far can each dragon breathe fire?

Petunia _____ yards   Snap _____ yards

Daisy _____ yards   Rosebud _____ yards

Which dragon can breathe fire the farthest? _____

Answers on page 72

How Much Is That?

Objective: Learning about money

What You Need:

a copy of the **reproducible** on page 75 for each child

real coins or play-money coins of each denomination

a small box or bag

small containers marked 1¢, 5¢, 10¢, 25¢

small objects with price tags marked under a dollar

What You Do:

1. Place a variety of real coins or play-money coins in a small box or bag. Line up the containers labeled with cent marks. Show one coin of each denomination to the class and ask students to tell you its name and value. Then have volunteers blindly select one coin from the box, tell its name and value, and place it in the correct container. Continue until all the coins have been sorted.

2. Now place all the coins back into the box. Display the small items on which you have placed price tags. Organize the children into small groups. One child from each group takes a handful of coins from the box. The group can sort and count the money. When the group has determined the total value of the coins, the children can examine the items "for sale." Ask them to list which single items they could buy and which single items they could not buy with their money.

3. For more practice with money, distribute copies of the **reproducible** on page 75 and read the directions aloud before children complete the sheets on their own.

Answers for page 75: 32¢ buys either: car, paintbrush, plant, socks, baseball, sailboat, or necklace.
63¢ buys either: light bulb, mittens, cap, pear, gum, or fishbowl.

Name_____ Date_____

Going Shopping

You have the coins at the left. Circle the choices of things you could buy with that money. Which thing in each group would you choose to buy?

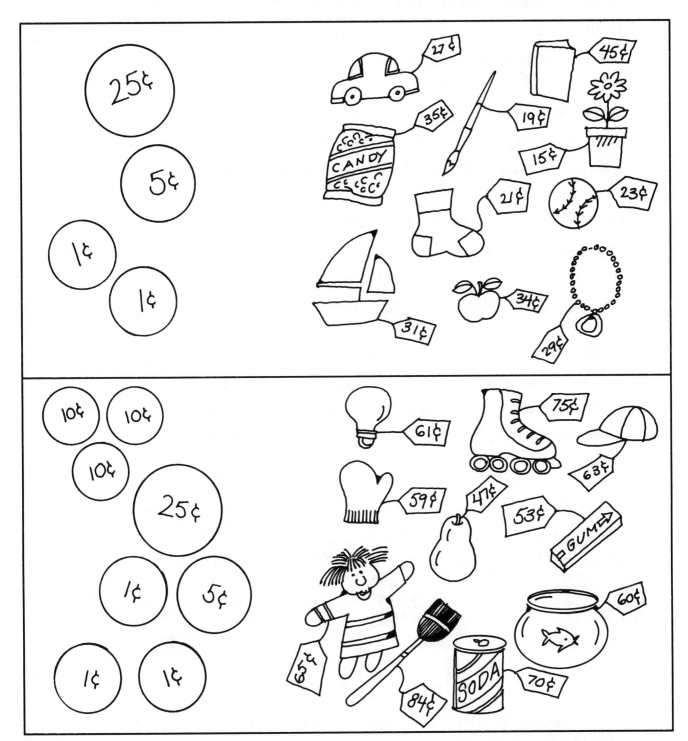

Answers on page 74

■ 75 ■

Money, Money

Objective: Budgeting money

What You Need:

a copy of the **reproducible** on page 77 for each child

small objects with price tags (recycle items from previous activity)

several calculators for sharing

What You Do:

1. Display several small objects with price tags. Select two items and tell the children, "I would like to buy both these things. How much will they cost? How much money do I need to have? How can I find out?" The children should respond that you can add the two prices together to find how much it will cost to buy both items. Allow volunteers to use calculators to find the answer. Repeat the activity several times using different combinations of items.

2. Now distribute copies of the **reproducible** on page 77. Read the directions aloud before children begin working individually. Allow students to use calculators to answer the questions. For the question about Goldilocks, have children compare their selections and total costs.

Answers for page 77: Mama Bear = $13.72, Papa Bear = $10.58, Baby Bear = $6.80, Goldilocks = Answers will vary.

Name_____ Date_____

Three Bears Go Buying

Goldilocks and the three bears are going shopping. How much money do they need to buy what they want?

Mama Bear wants a big chair, a big bowl, and a big bed. She needs _____.

Baby Bear wants a little chair, a little bowl, and a little bed. He needs _____.

Papa Bear wants a medium chair, a medium bowl, and a medium bed. He needs _____.

Goldilocks wants a comfortable chair, a pretty bowl, and a fluffy bed. She needs _____.

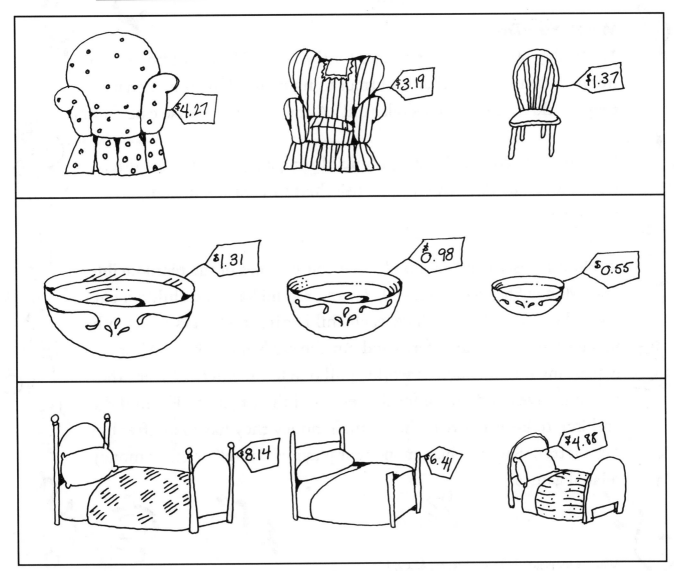

$4.27 $3.19 $1.37

$1.31 $0.98 $0.55

$8.14 $6.41 $4.88

Answers on page 76

Making Change

Objective: Learning to subtract money

What You Need:

a copy of the **reproducible** on page 79 for each child

a copy of the **reproducibles** on pages 80, 81, and 82 for each child

small objects with price tags under $1.00

calculators

index cards

a small box or bag

What You Do:

1. Display objects with price tags for the class. Have children select items to "buy." Help them subtract to figure out how much change they would get from a one-dollar bill. Allow students to use calculators.

2. Distribute copies of the **reproducible** on page 79. Read the directions aloud and then let children use their calculators to complete the pages.

3. Hold a classroom "auction." Distribute copies of the **reproducible** Play-Money Sheets on pages 80, 81, and 82 and have the children cut apart their "bills." Then have each child write the letters of his or her name on separate index cards and put the cards into a box. After explaining how an auction works, pull one letter at a time from the box and have children bid for the letters of their names. Remind the children to keep an eye on how much money they have left after buying a letter. Save the play money for playing "store" or other money-related games.

Answers for page 79: $1.22, 19¢, 8¢, $2.69, 17¢, 6¢

Name_____ Date_____

How Much Change?

Prunella and Percy Pigg went shopping. Figure out how much change they got for each item.

Prunella bought	She paid with	She got this much change.
$3.78	$5.00	_____
Percy bought	He paid with	He got this much change.
$1.56	$1.00 25¢ 25¢ 25¢	_____
Prunella bought	She paid with	She got this much change
$1.17	$1.00 25¢	_____
Percy bought	He paid with	He got this much change.
$2.31	$5.00	_____
Prunella bought	She paid with	She got this much change.
$4.08	$1.00 $1.00 $1.00 $1.00 25¢	_____
Percy bought	He paid with	He got this much change.
$3.49	$1.00 $1.00 $1.00 25¢ 10¢ 10¢ 10¢	_____

Answers on page 78

Play-Money Sheet

Play-Money Sheet

Play-Money Sheet

Tick, Tock

Objective: Learning about time in minutes

What You Need:

a copy of the **reproducible** on page 84 for each child

a watch with a second hand or a 1-minute "hourglass"

a large clock with a sweeping second hand

What You Do:

1. Ask the class: "How long is a minute?" The children might respond that a minute is sixty seconds long. Ask the children to close their eyes and then raise their hands when they think a minute has passed from the time you say: "Go!" Start watching the second hand on your watch or turn over an "hourglass" at the same time. Watch for the first and last children to raise their hands to get the shortest and longest "minutes."

2. Now have the children look at a clock with a second hand. As the second hand makes one full sweep, count off the seconds out loud. Tell students that exactly one minute has passed. Then repeat step 1.

3. To reinforce the concept of a minute, distribute copies of the **reproducible** on page 84. Read the directions aloud. Then tell the class that you will be the timekeeper. Be sure everyone can hear you say "start" and "stop" for each activity. Tell children to count softly as they do each activity. Give them a few moments between each activity to record their personal results and compare results with each other.

Name_____ **Date**_____

How Many Times?

What can you do in one minute? Count how many times you can do these things. Write your answers below.

Clap your hands _____ times	**Say the alphabet** _____ times
Hop on one foot _____ times	**Touch your toes** _____ times
Walk around your desk _____ times	**Blink your eyes** _____ times
Write your name _____ times	**Write your telephone number** _____ times

Hickory, Dickory

Objective: Reading digital and analog clocks

What You Need:

a copy of the **reproducible** on page 87 for each child

tagboard

scissors

an analog clock

What You Do:

1. Here's how to make a toy digital clock: First, cut three long strips from tagboard. Write the numbers from 0 to 9 vertically on two strips and the numbers 0 to 5 on another strip, leaving some room at either end of each strip. Then cut two shorter strips with one dot on one and the number 1 on the other.

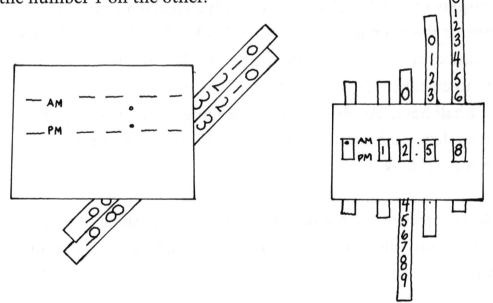

2. Make the clock itself from another sheet of tagboard. Make two horizontal rows of five slits each across the tagboard (see illustration). Then mark AM and PM between the first and second pairs of slits from the left (see illustration). Place a colon (:) between the second and third pairs of slits from the right.

3. Now thread each number strip vertically through the two rows of slits (see illustration). The strip with the dot should be threaded through the two slits on the far lefthand side. Next comes the strip with the 1, then one of the strips marked 0 to 9, then the strip marked 0 to 5, and, finally, the other strip marked 0 to 9 (see illustration).

4. Discuss the concepts of A.M. and P.M. with the children. Tell them that A.M. means from midnight to noon (morning), while P.M. indicates the hours from noon to midnight (afternoon and evening). Ask the children to name some of the things they might do in the morning (get out of bed, eat breakfast, go to school) and the afternoon or evening (get home from school, eat supper, watch television, go to sleep). Encourage children to name times on the hour or half hour, such as 8:00 A.M. or 6:30 P.M. Ask volunteers to set the digital "clock" for these school and home activities.

5. Now display the analog clock and teach the children to read the same times on the hour and half hour on this kind of clock. Tell them that this kind of clock does not show whether the time is A.M. or P.M. Have volunteers take turns setting both clocks for the same times on the hour or half hour. As children become more adept at telling time, you can introduce such conversions as 1:45 digital time = "a quarter to 2" on the analog clock.

6. Distribute copies of the **reproducible** on page 87 to the children. Read the directions aloud before the children complete the sheets on their own.

Name_____ Date_____

It's About Time!

Draw lines to match the clocks that tell the same time.

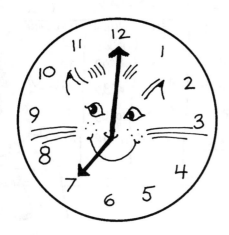 

| 11:00 | 7:00 | 10:30 | 5:30 |

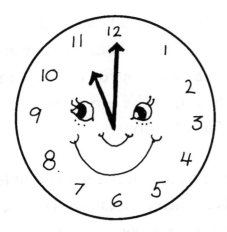 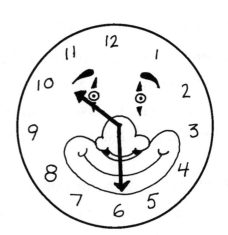

The Mouse Ran Up the Clock

Objective: Calculating elapsed time

What You Need:

a copy of the **reproducible** on
 page 89 for each child

a digital clock

an analog clock

scissors

a paper fastener (brad) for each child

ACTIVITY	WHEN IT STARTS	WHEN IT ENDS	HOW LONG IT LASTS
MATH	8:30	9:00	30
ENGLISH	9:00	9:30	30
ART	9:30	10:30	1
RECESS	10:30	11:00	30 M

SCHEDULE FOR TODAY

What You Do:

1. Give children this problem: "If you started watching TV at
7:00 P.M. and stopped watching at 8:00 P.M., how long did you watch
TV?" (1 hour, or 60 minutes) Show what this passage of time looks
like on a digital clock as you make it count off each minute until the
hour changes. Then show the same passage of time on an analog clock,
as you move the minute hand all the way around until the hour hand
moves to the next hour.

2. Now ask: "What if you started watching TV at 7:00 P.M. and
stopped at 7:30? How long did you watch TV?" (1/2 hour, or 30 minutes) Again, show what this passage of time looks like on a digital and
an analog clock. Use the same steps to show that the time elapsed
between 7:00 P.M. and 8:30 P.M. is 1 hour and 30 minutes.

3. Have children cut out the clock face and hands on the **reproducible**
on page 89. Use brads to fasten the hands to the clock faces. Then set
up a schedule for the next day in which each classroom activity begins
on the hour or half hour. Have children use their clocks to figure out
how long each activity will last.

The Face of Time

Cut out the clock face and the hands. Attach the hands to the face with a brad. Use your clock to measure how much time your school activities take.

All in a Year's Work

Objective: Using a calendar

What You Need:

a copy of the **reproducible** on page 91 for each child

a large calendar for this year

masking tape

a pad of square stick-on notes

What You Do:

1. Review the names of the days of the week and the months of the year. Have children practice reciting the names of the days and months in the correct order.

2. Now display a large calendar for this year. Ask each child to tell the month and date of his or her birthday and find that date on the calendar.

3. For more fun with dates, make a class calendar for the bulletin board. Have children use masking tape to make a grid seven spaces wide and six spaces long on the bulletin board. Leave space at the top for the name of the month and the days of the week. Attach stick-on notes inside the grid to show the date of each day and to note events such as birthdays and class trips that are coming up that month.

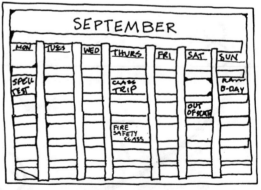

4. Distribute copies of the **reproducible** on page 91. Review the directions together with the class. Then have children work individually to complete the page.

Answers for page 91: 1. Tuesdays   2. Fridays
3. Thursday, Oct. 11   4. Monday, Oct. 22   5. Saturday, Oct. 6

Name_____ Date_____

Which Day?

Look at Wizard Murphy's calendar. Then answer the questions about Wizard Murphy's busy days.

Sunday	Monday	Tuesday	Wednesday	Thursday	Friday	Saturday
	1	2	3	4	5 SEE KING	6 COLLECT SNAKE EARS
7	8	9 practice magic spells	10	11	12 SEE KING	13
14	15	16 practice magic spells	17	18	19 SEE KING	20
21	22 collect bat toes	23 practice magic spells	24	25	26 SEE KING	27
28	29	30 practice magic spells	31 HALLOWEEN			

1. On what days does Murphy practice his magic spells? _____

2. On what days does Murphy see the King? _____

3. On what day is Murphy's birthday? _____

4. On what day does Murphy plan to go bat-toe collecting? _____

5. On what day does Murphy plan to go snake-ear collecting? _____

Answers on page 90

It's on the Table

Objective: Understanding information tables and graphs

What You Need:

1 copy each of the **reproducibles** on pages 93, 94, and 95 for each pair of children

a sheet of tagboard

What You Do:

1. Tell the children that you want to find out how many of them like different kinds of pets. Explain that one way to do this is to make a table or chart showing each person's favorite.

2. Display a large sheet of tagboard. Across the top, write these headings: PET, HOW MANY LIKE IT BEST, and TOTAL. Then draw vertical lines to make three columns (see illustration). Now have children take turns naming their favorite pets. Write each new entry on the chart, and add tally marks each time another child names that pet. When the first two columns are complete, have children count the tally marks and write in the total numbers in the third column.

3. Now use the Favorite Pet chart to ask some simple addition and subtraction problems. Ask questions such as, "How many more children like cats than like snakes?" "How many fewer children like dogs than like gerbils?" These are quick questions that can be asked during odd moments in the classroom for reinforcement of addition and subtraction skills.

4. For more fun with charts, distribute one copy of the **reproducible** on page 93 to each pair of children. Read the directions aloud before the partners begin their interviews. Children will enjoy gathering other kinds of information on the **reproducibles** on pages 94 and 95.

Names_____ Date_____ ▪ 93 ▪

Favorite Colors

What is the most popular color in your class? Ask each classmate to make a mark next to his or her favorite color. Add up the marks for each color and put the numbers in the Total column. Which color gets the most votes?

Color	How many like it best	Total
Red		
Blue		
Orange		
Pink		
Green		
Yellow		
Black		
Purple		
Brown		

Names_____ Date_____

Favorite Desserts

Ask your classmates to pick their favorite desserts. Draw a small smiley face for each answer.

 = **1 person likes it best**

Dessert	How many like it best	Total
Ice Cream		
Cake		
Apple Pie		
Cherry Pie		
Candy Bar		
Cheese		
Brussel Sprouts		

Names_____ Date_____

Favorite Sports

Ask your classmates what their favorite sports are. Fill in a space for each answer. If someone's favorite sport is not listed, fill in the column labeled Other Sport.

	Soccer	Baseball	Softball	Ice Skating	Roller Blading	Bicycling	Swimming	Gymnastics	Other Sport
10									
9									
8									
7									
6									
5									
4									
3									
2									
1									

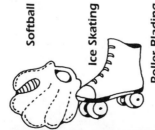

■ 95 ■